AF594626
Jolly Phonics
Handwriting Book 4
ai j oa ie ee or
in print letters

# Guidelines

Good pencil control and correct formation enable students to achieve neat, fluent and, eventually, joined handwriting.

Handwriting practice works best when the students are sitting at their table or desk. This provides a firm flat surface to write on and encourages correct posture.

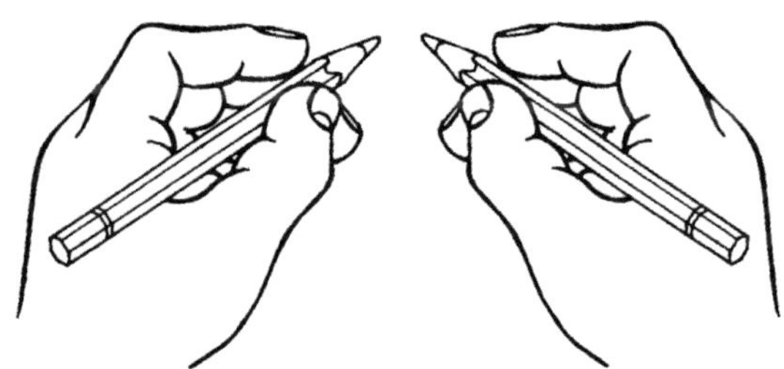

A good pencil hold from the very beginning is extremely important for developing neat, fluent handwriting. The tripod pencil grip is recommended.

Hold the pencil between the thumb and index finger, and support it on the middle finger. As the pencil is moved, the knuckles on the thumb and index finger look like a frog's legs.

Coloring is also a good way to develop fine motor skills. Encourage the students to color carefully, to keep within the lines, and to choose appropriate colors.

**Spot the frog**

Encourage the students to look out for the frog throughout these books, to remind them to practice their 'froggy-leg' grip.

Write your name on the robot and draw your face on the screen.

Match the top halves of the pictures to the bottom halves. The first one has been done.

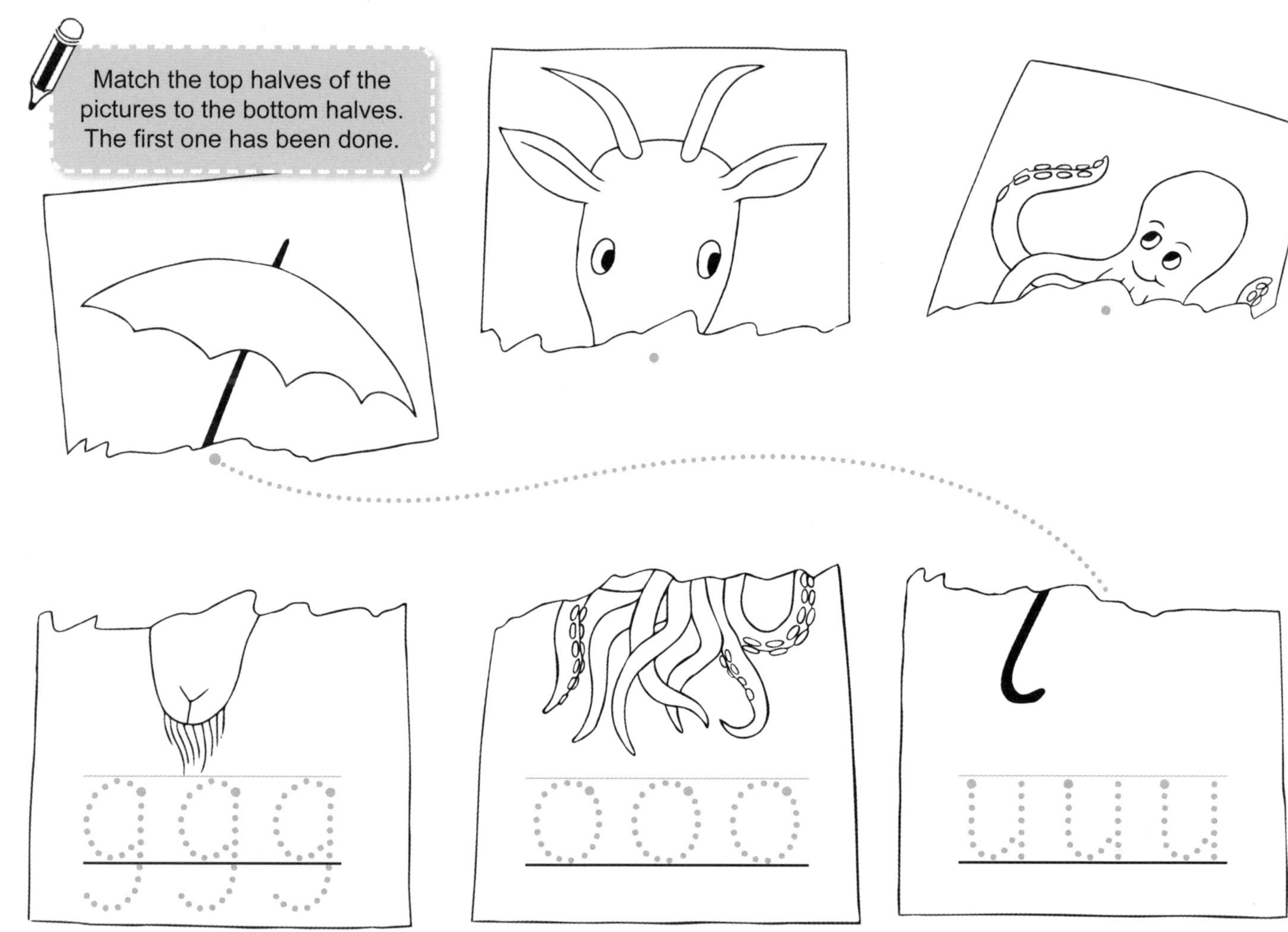

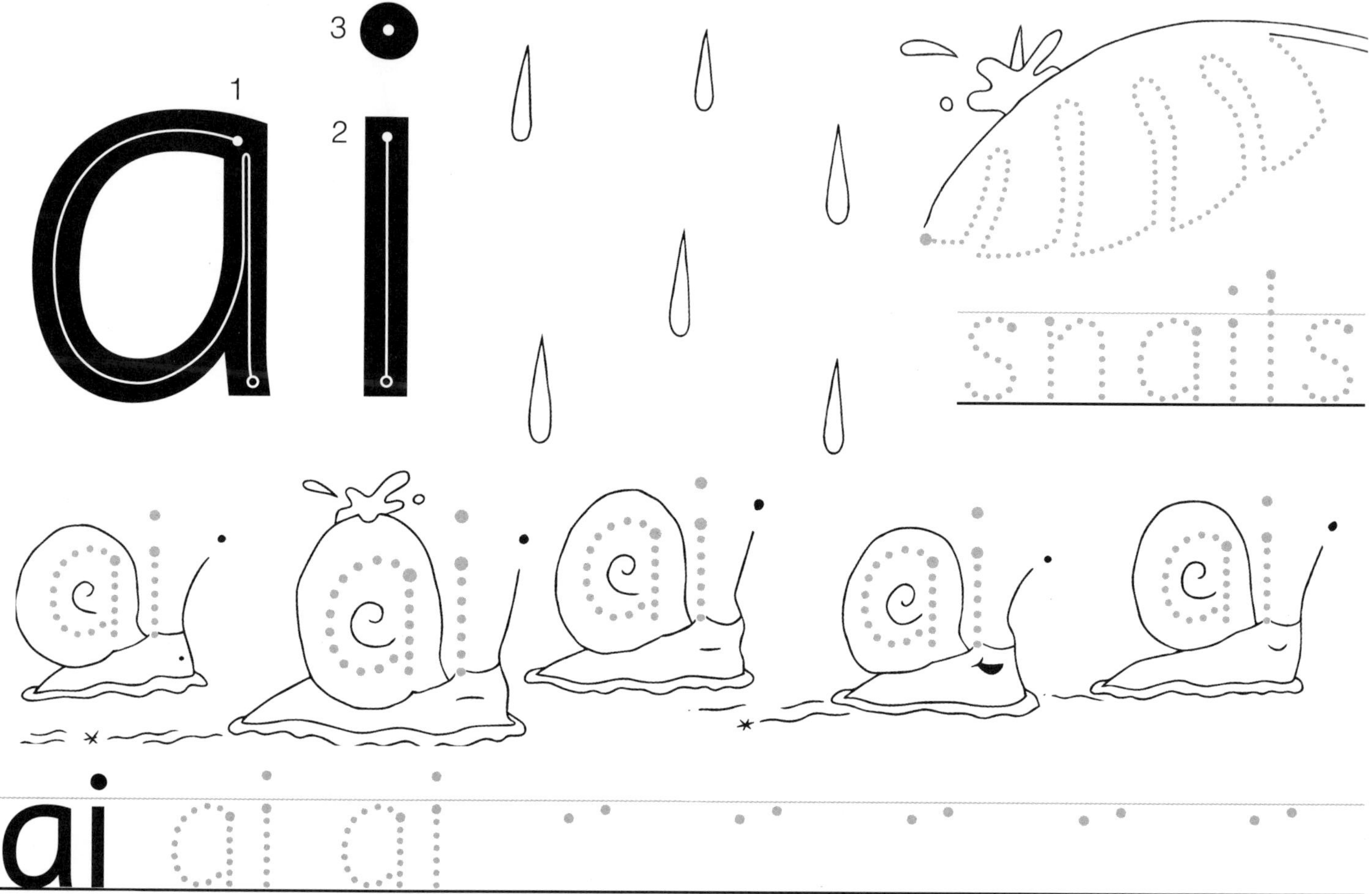
1
2
3
ai
snails
ai

tails
Which animals do these tails belong to?

2
1
j

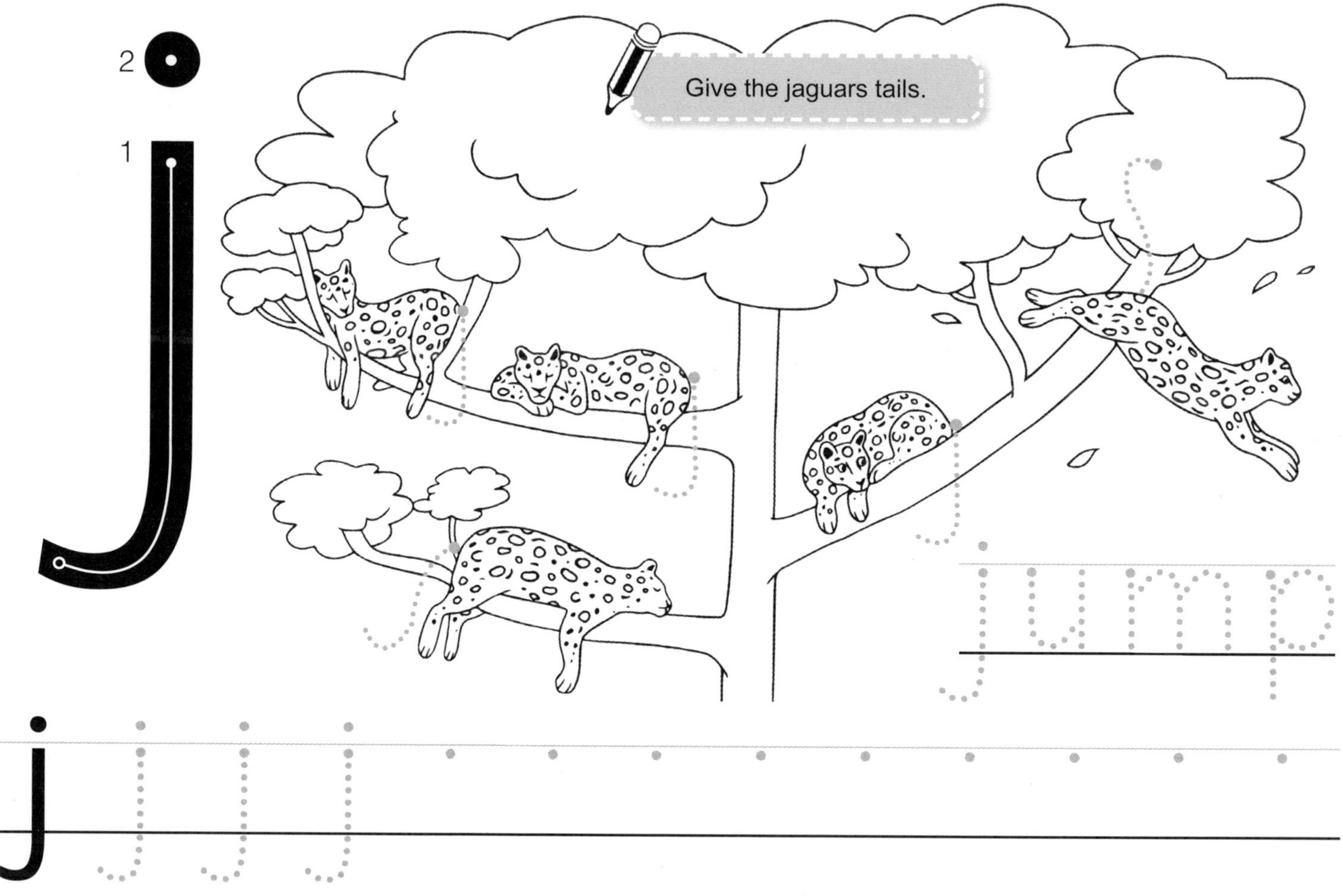


j

Match the jigsaw pictures to the starting sounds.

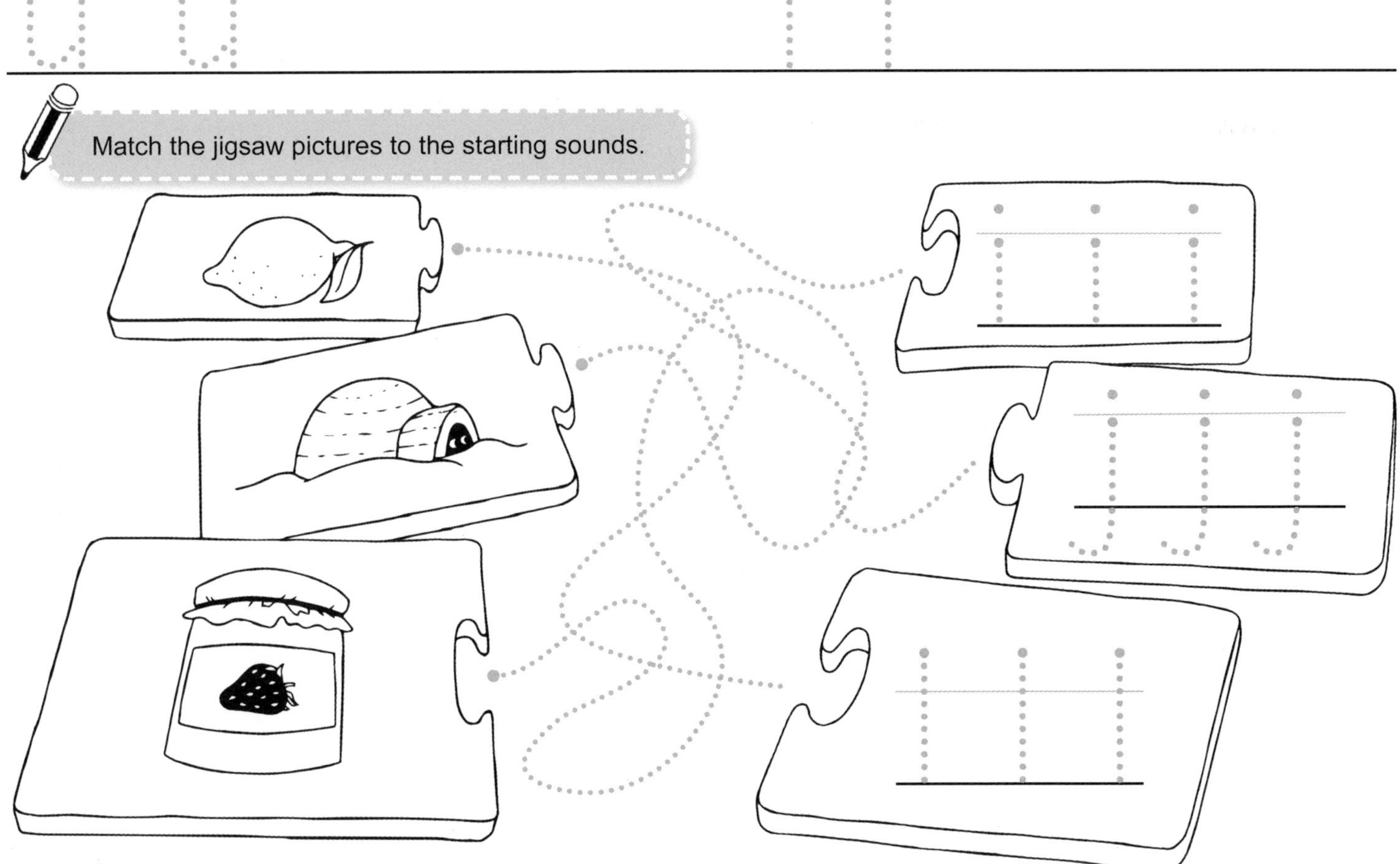

oa

Follow the lines to see which boat wins first prize.

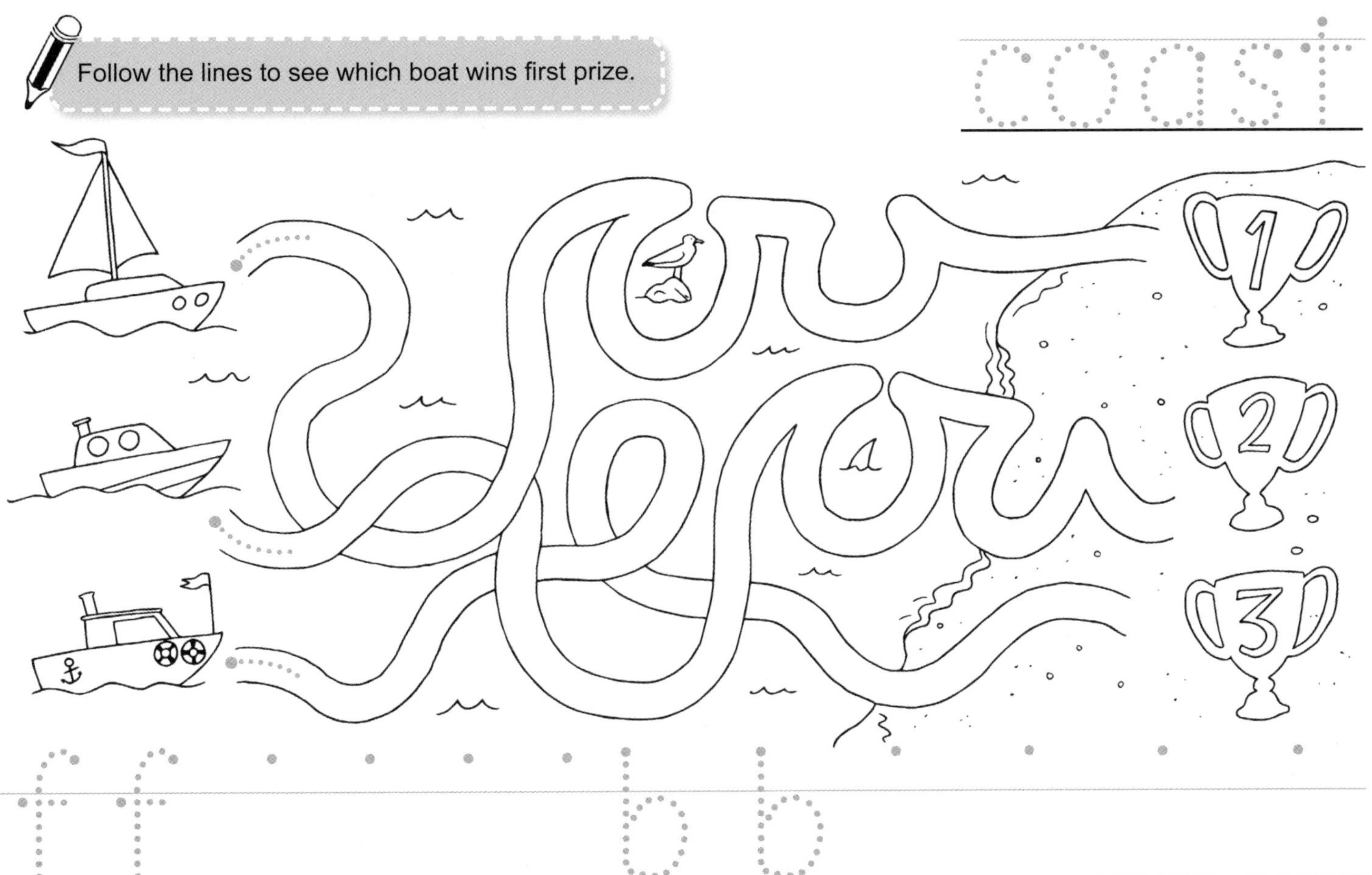

Help the cars get through the traffic cones.

a big road

a traffic jam

2
1
3
ie
magpie
Help the magpie get back to the nest to feed its chick.
ie

c c k k

pies

Match the pie slices to the pie they came from.

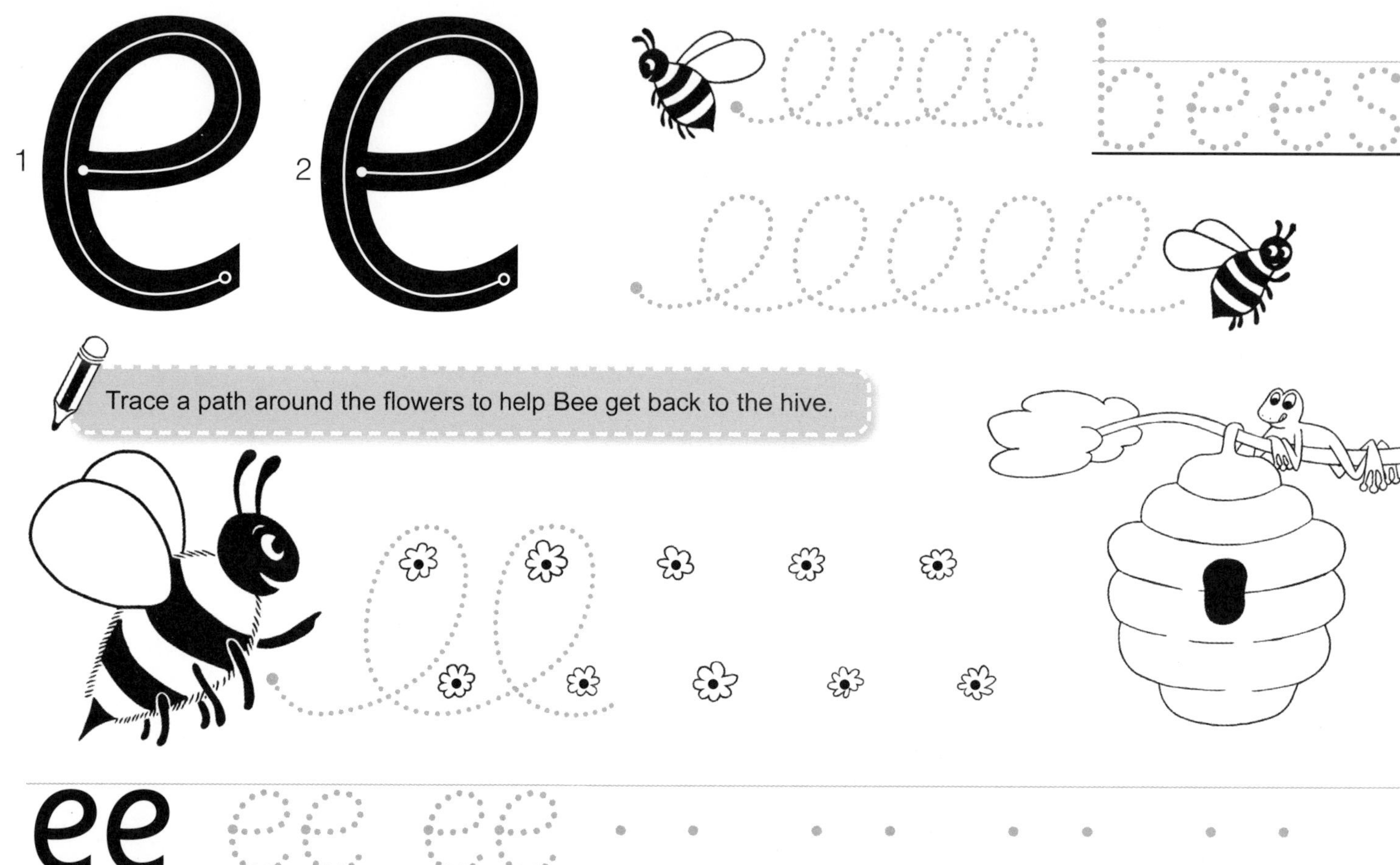


Trace a path around the flowers to help Bee get back to the hive.

ee

e e . . . h h . . .

trees

How many sheep can you see hiding under the trees?

1
2
or
for
or or or

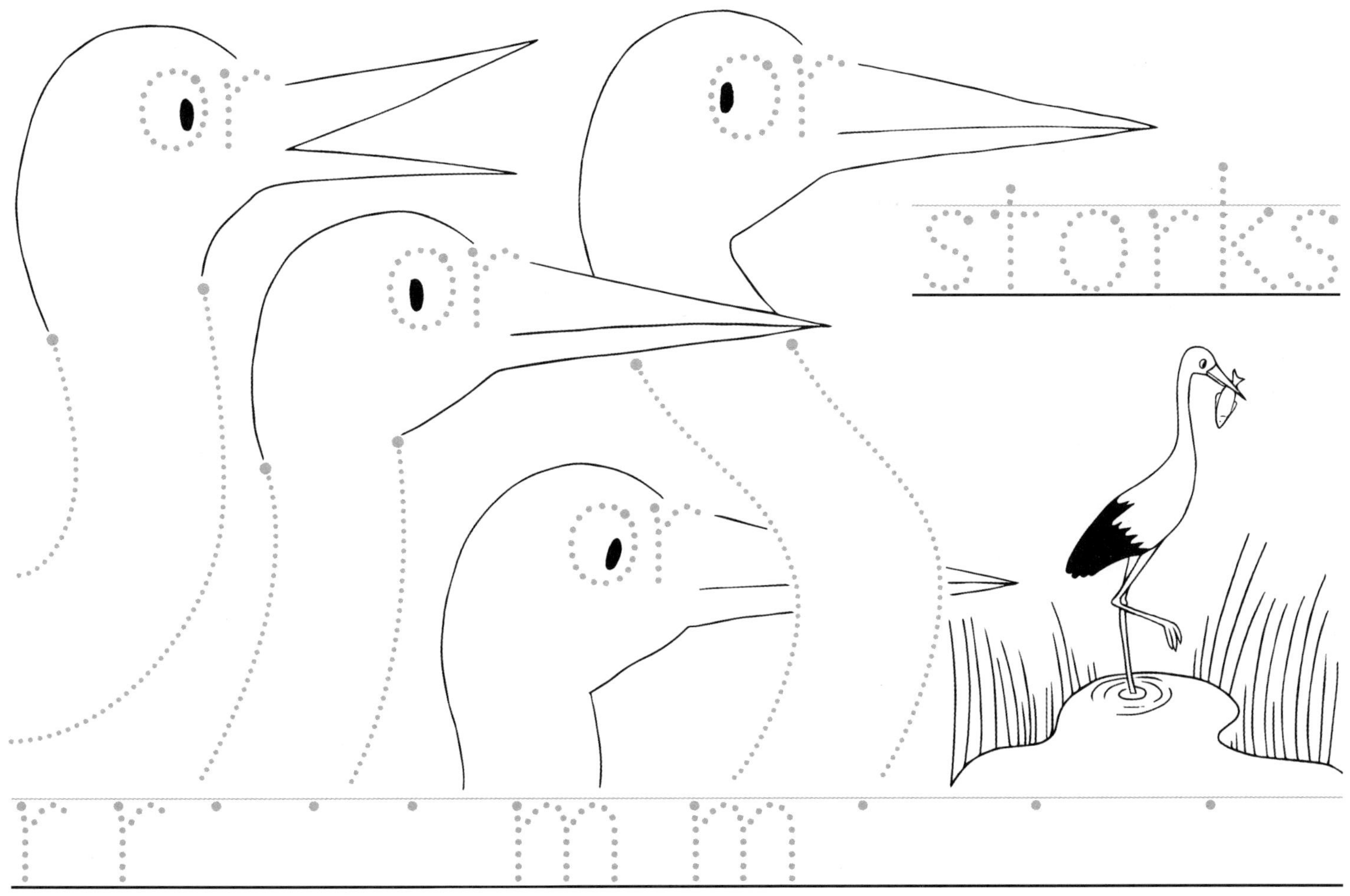


r r m m

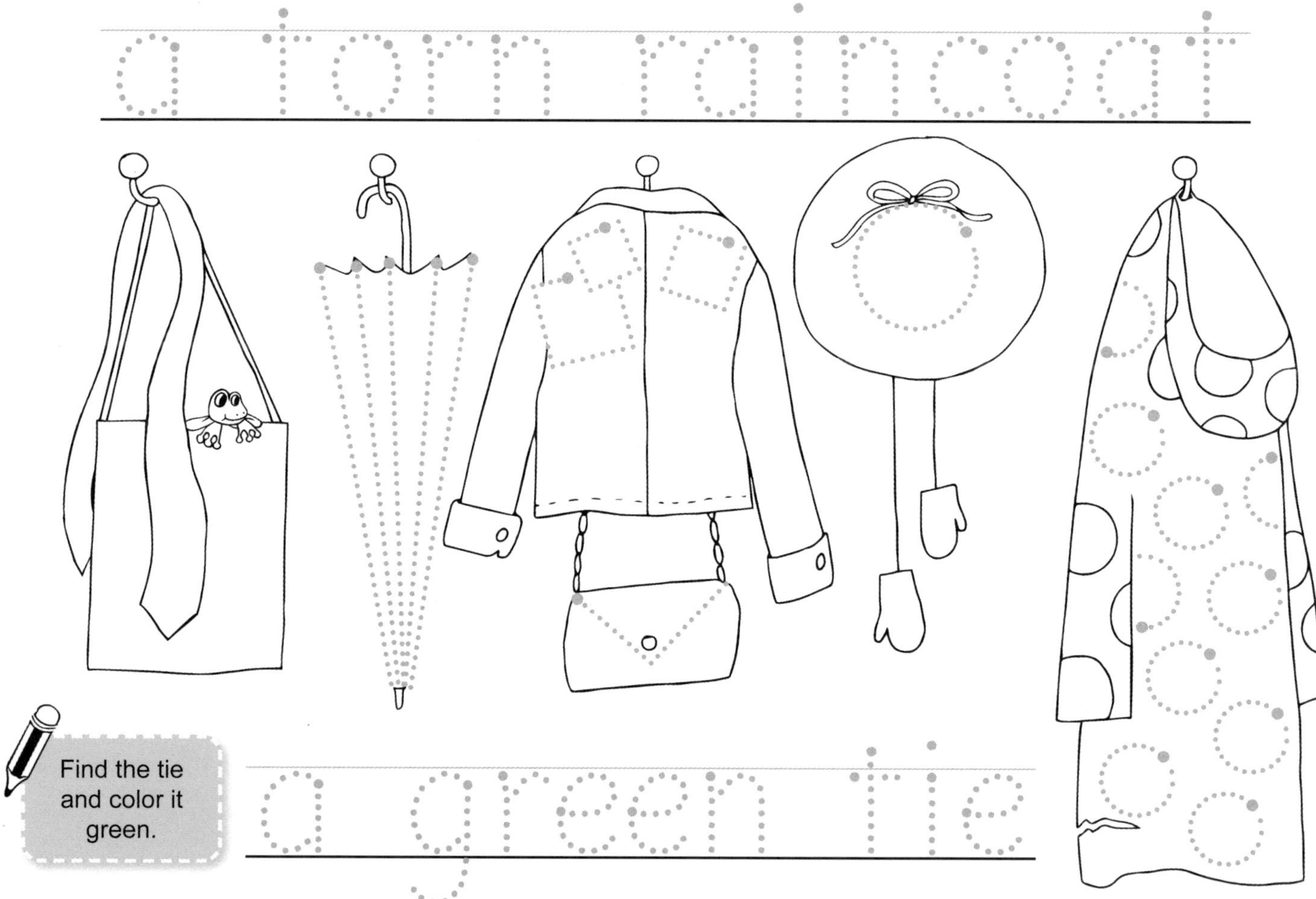
a torn raincoat
Find the tie and color it green.
a green tie

trees in a storm

Which clothing would you wear in a storm?

Can you draw something that includes each sound?

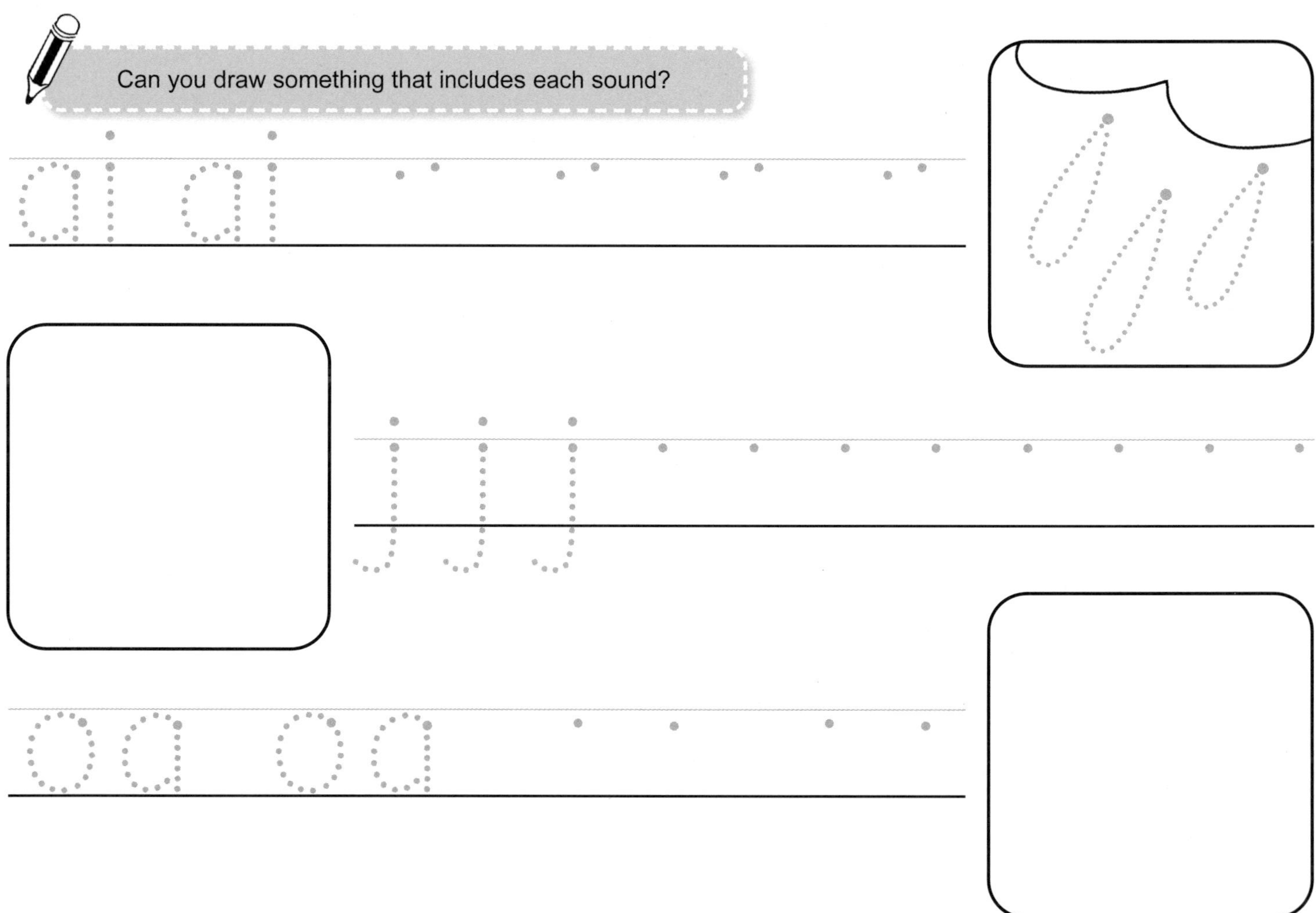

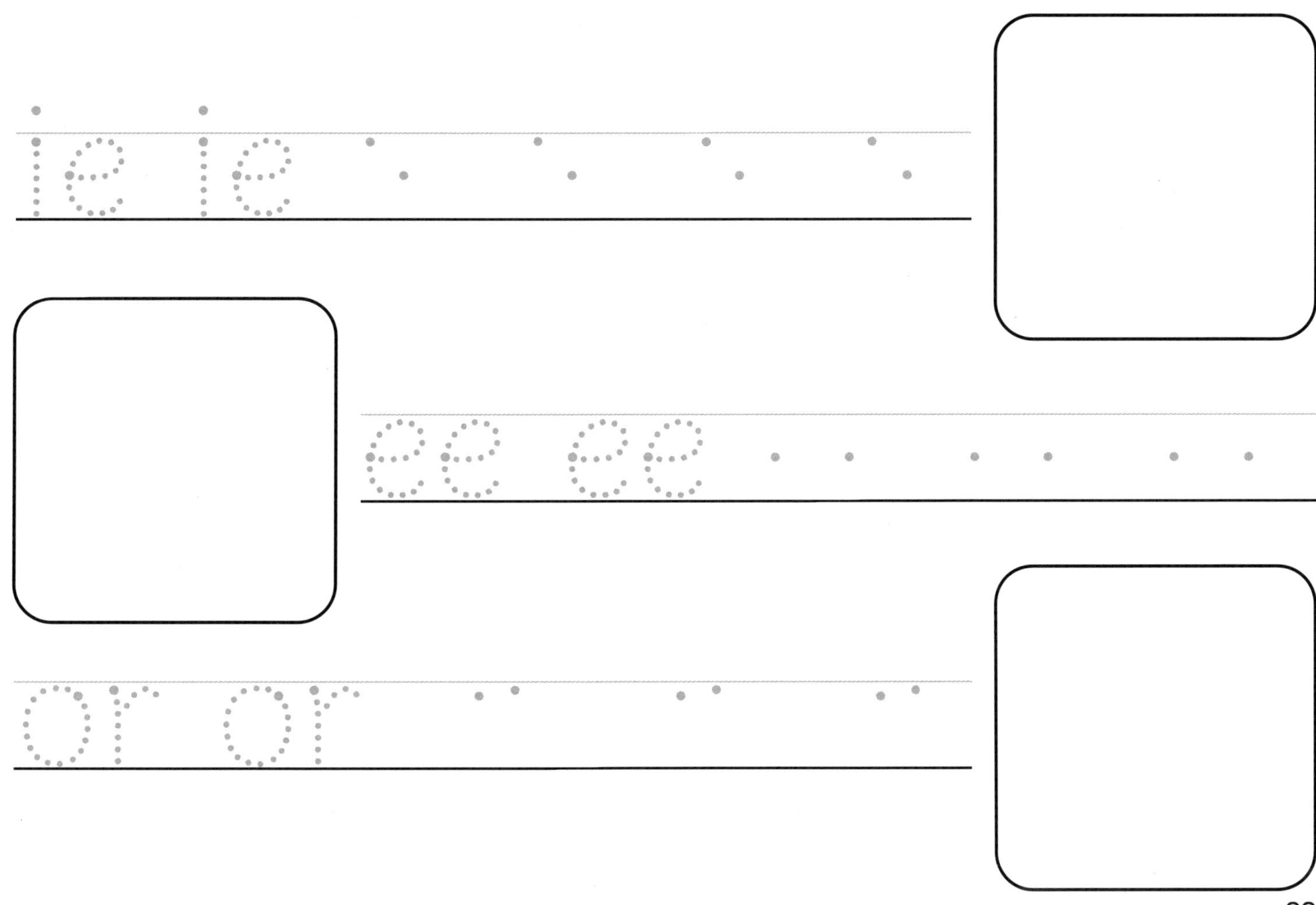
ie ie
ee ee
or or

Ages 4+

# Jolly Phonics Handwriting Book

## Perfect for practicing letter formation

These handwriting books provide letter formation practice for beginner writers. Dotted letters and words (with starting dots) remind students how the letters are formed, and encourage them to write words using the letter sounds they know. Each page features fun activities to complete and attractive pictures to color, which help the students to develop fine motor control.

This book contains the following letter sounds:

| | |
|---|---|
| Group 1: | s a t i p n |
| Group 2: | c k e h r m d |
| Group 3: | g o u l f b |
| Group 4: | ai j oa ie ee or |
| Group 5: | z w ng v oo oo |
| Group 6: | y x ch sh th th |
| Group 7: | qu ou oi ue er ar |

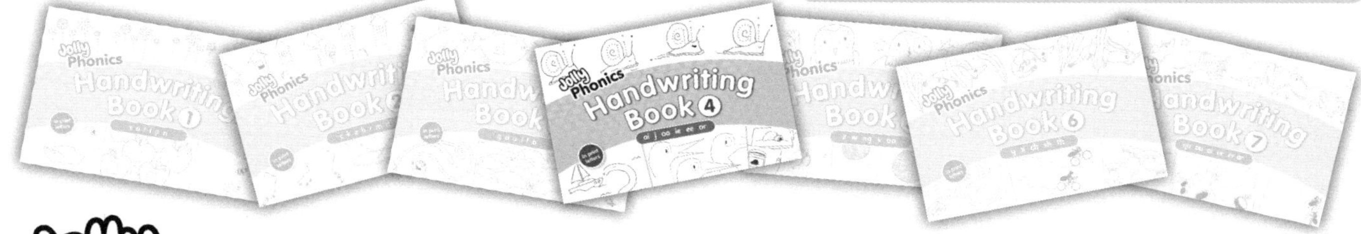

To see the full range of Jolly Phonics products, visit our website at www.jollylearning.com

MIX
Paper | Supporting responsible forestry
FSC® C016973

ISBN 978-1-83582-184-8

Reference: JL1848


82 Winter Sport Lane, Williston, VT 05495, USA. Tel: +1-800-488-2665
77 Hornbeam Road, Buckhurst Hill, Essex, IG9 6JX, UK. Tel: +44 20 8501 0405
Printed in China. 

www.jollylearning.com info@jollylearning.co.uk